The Beautiful
PLANTS
of
KENYA

John Karmali

Text Book Centre

For Joseph and Sembene, our dear grandsons

This edition published 1993 by
Text Book Centre Ltd.
Kijabe Street,
P.O. Box 47540
Nairobi
Kenya

First published 1988

Second Impression 1993

Copyright: John Karmali and Camerapix 1988

ISBN 1 874041 21 0

Designed and produced by
Camerapix Publishers International,
P. O. Box 45048,
Nairobi, Kenya

Text edited by Joan Karmali and Shereen Karmali

Designed by Craig Dodd

Printed in Hong Kong by South China Printing Co.

*Half-title: The exotic Australian Flame Tree in full
glorious blossom. Title page: Golden Wattle with its
attractive mimosa-like blooms. Contents page: The mass
of delicate pink flowers of the Himalayan Bird Cherry.*

Contents

Preface

As was the case with my *Beautiful Birds of Kenya*, this is *not* a field guide. Its main purpose is to illustrate and identify some of the colourful plants which readily attract the eye of visitors and residents alike, and which help to make this country of Kenya so beautiful.

Varying habitats from sea-level to the height of Mount Kenya, and the different seasons from heavy rainfall to brilliant sunshine, all contribute to making the land readily suitable for a vast range of flora. Some of them are indigenous and others imported from countries as far away as Australia, tropical America and Asia. They flourish and flower in their appropriate environment and make the country lovely to behold.

The format and size of the book have imposed certain limitations in the selection of species included. What to leave out has been the main problem, and the final choice has been somewhat arbitrary and one of personal preference. It is hoped, however, that the compilation will supply a long-felt need.

A work of this nature would not have been possible without the unstinting co-operation of a number of keen gardeners and friends and I wish to express my special appreciation to Henk Beentje, Geoffrey Mungai, Jean Hayes, Sue Sylvester and Daphne Sheppard. My grateful thanks are also due to Ann Birnie, Aruna Chandaria, Mary Edwards, Gaby Remnant, Mary Ridley and Mike and Loretta Tremlett. Finally, my task has been made considerably easier by the devoted support of my wife Joan and daughter Shereen.

Introduction

The wild landscapes of Kenya are, to a large extent, characterized by their trees. Rivers in the drier areas are lined with doum palms and large Acacias; the foothills of the mountains are clothed in majestic forests; the plains of the great game parks are dotted with Baobabs and thorn trees. Man-made, or man-influenced, landscapes are also much influenced by trees; try to imagine Nairobi without its trees, and you would see a most desolate environment of steel, cement and glass. The lush gardens of the suburbs are dominated by the splendid Jacaranda and various other exotic species, as well as by indigenous ones. And the famous hotels of the Coast – where would they be without their whispering palms?

But it is not just the beauty of the trees that appeals to the Kenyan. Trees provide part of his or her diet, wood for building and implements, firewood, fodder for animals, medicines, dyes, shade for the crop . . . the list is endless. The nomadic peoples of the drier areas use branches of thorn trees to construct the defensive walls of their *bomas*, or cattle enclosures. On their long marches across the parched plains, these nomads can spot certain trees in the distance that promise water and a good camping site. Branches of these same trees will provide the firesticks that, when rubbed together, will light their fires.

But not only do trees influence landscapes and people, they are influenced by them in their turn. Landscape determines which trees will grow. For instance, you will never find a Baobab in the highlands, nor a yellow-barked Fever Tree away from water. Each environment, or habitat, has its own trees peculiar to that habitat, and very few of these will grow in different habitats. The rather dry forests around Nairobi support tree species that are entirely different from the rain forest of Western Kenya, or from the wet coastal forests. And even within Tsavo, the trees lining Tsavo River are quite different from those a hundred meters away from the river. Man or woman influences the trees by planting them around the homestead, by cutting them down to make way for agriculture, by introducing them to areas where they did not grow before ...

Although there is no gainsaying the fact that cities like Nairobi and Mombasa are made beautiful by trees from places as far away as South America and Australia, personally I prefer true Kenyans such as the Baobab, the Figs, the magnificent Camphor Tree, and the high-altitude Hagenia. John Karmali has taken on the difficult task of selecting the more conspicuous of the more than eight hundred wild Kenyan species, as well as some famous exotics. Such a selection can, of course, only give an idea of the fantastic variety of trees to be found in Kenya, which is so rich in nature. But this selection is illustrated in such an enchanting way that it whets the appetite for more, and it opens the eye to one more of the aspects of this great country: its beautiful trees.

Dr Henk Beentje
Senior Research Fellow
The Herbarium
Nairobi National Museum

1 PALMS

Coconut Palm

Cocos nucifera
Family: Palmae

The original home of the coconut is a mystery. Some authorities consider it to be Polynesia, while others maintain that it came from South America, whence began its journey westwards drifting in ocean currents across the Pacific to reach the shores of Africa thousands of years ago. Undoubtedly this palm has thrived on the Kenya coast for many years.

Although mainly restricted to coastal regions where conditions are ideal for its growth, it has been introduced with limited success on the shores of Lake Victoria and other upcountry areas.

Besides forming a significant part of the coastal diet, the nut providing valuable food and drink, it has many other uses. The fibre of the husk is used for making ropes, mats, or stuffing mattresses; the shell of the nut makes charcoal; the leaves are used for thatching houses or weaving into baskets and mats; and the trunk for building houses.

But the major economic importance of the coconut is the dried flesh of the mature nut known as copra, which is processed to yield coconut oil for cooking, and coconut meal, a valuable high protein food for livestock.

Illustrated on following page

Doum Palm

Hyphaene coriacea
Family: Palmae

This indigenous palm is the only member of its family which branches. The long slender stem and branches divide regularly into two (dichotomously), giving the tree its distinctive appearance as it often overtops the surrounding vegetation to reach a height of over 50 ft. (15 m.).

The three-cornered orangey-brown fruit, about 3 in. (8 cm.) long, has an outer layer which is edible, but is not very palatable to humans. It is often swallowed by elephants, thus helping the plant's dispersal.

The leaves are used for weaving baskets and mats, and the fruit for production of buttons and necklaces.

Illustrated on previous page

Date Palm

Phoenix spp.
Family: Palmae

The Wild Date Palm (*P. reclinata*) is widely distributed in Kenya, where it thrives in groups in the hotter and drier areas of the country along streams and swamps, a high water-table being essential. Its fruit is edible but not very exciting.

The commercially cultivated variety of Date Palm (*P. dactylifera*) has a bigger, fleshier and more palatable fruit. This has long been a major source of food for the people who live in the desert areas of the Middle East and North Africa. Introduced into Kenya in the first instance by Arab traders, the Date Palm has considerable potential as a source of food in areas such as Garissa, near the Tana River and the shores of Lake Turkana.

The leaves of the Date Palm are often used to produce baskets and sleeping mats.

Illustrated on following page

2 ORNAMENTAL TREES

Golden Wattle, Mimosa

Acacia podolyriifolia
Family: Mimosaceae

An importation from Australia, this member of the Acacia family does not bear spines. It is a very striking smallish tree with its grey-green foliage and mimosa-like rich yellow flowers. Ideal for gardens, it is widespread and common.

Illustrated on previous page and title page

Thorn Trees

Acacia spp.
Family: Mimosaceae

There are 42 indigenous species of Acacia distributed throughout Kenya. Their identification as members of the Acacia family is readily made because of the presence of spines. Recognition of individual species is much more difficult, many of them requiring close examination of the flowers and leaves in a botanical laboratory.

Red Thorn

Acacia lahai

This is a flat-topped tree which reaches a height of about 50 ft. (15 m.). Its spines are flattened on the upper side, white, straight and about 2 in. (5 cm.) long. The red wood is extremely hard and durable, and very heavy. It is therefore mainly used for pulley blocks, fence posts, bridge timbers and rough farm buildings. It is found in various parts of the Rift Valley and elsewhere.

Illustrated on following page
Above: An Acacia sp. in flower
Below: Red Thorn

Fever Tree, Naivasha Thorn

Acacia xanthophloea

This is a tall flat-topped tree with a yellow powdery bark. The whitish straight spines are about $1\frac{1}{2}$ in. (4 cm.) long. Commonly found beside streams and lakes in the Rift Valley, especially at Lakes Naivasha and Nakuru.

Early travellers camping near these waters associated the tree with their going down with fever, hence the name Fever Tree. In fact, their illness was due to malaria transmitted by mosquitoes which breed on the edges of the lakes.

Acacia trees have a great variety of uses, besides being ornamental. Between them they provide shade, food for goats, wood-fuel, river-bank stabilization, fence posts, fix nitrogen as they drop their nutrient-rich leaves at the beginning of the rainy season, durable building material because of their resin content, hardwood suitable for carving, and tannin for the leather industry. *A. senegal* produces a high quality gum which has various industrial applications.

Illustrated on previous page

Above: An Acacia sp. in flower

Below: Fever Tree forest

Baobab

Adansonia digitata
Family: Bombacaceae

No traveller making his way south towards the coast from Nairobi can fail to have his curiosity and interest aroused by the first sight of this unique tree at altitudes below 4,000 ft. (1,300 m.). It has a glossy swollen trunk which may be as much as 15–20 ft. (5–7 m.) in diameter, though the whole tree may be only a little higher. Thick branches sprout from the top of the trunk, bearing a profusion of twigs.

The tree is bare of leaves through most of the dry season, particularly in areas where the rainfall is marginal. It is protected and worshipped in many parts of Africa, of which it is a native. Its white flowers are about 6 in. (15 cm.) wide and the oblong woody fruit, with a hard shell, is up to 12 in. (30 cm.) long.

Baobab has a variety of uses. The hollowed-out trunk can store water, the wood is used for making canoes, the bark fibre makes ropes and baskets, the leaves and fruit-pulp are used against fever, and the seeds and leaves are edible.

Illustrated on following page

Camel's Foot, Bauhinia

Bauhinia variegata
Family: Caesalpiniaceae

This plant from Asia takes its common name from the typical two-lobed leaves of the family which resemble a camel's foot. Its pink flowers are reminiscent of an orchid flower and the tree is therefore sometimes also known as the Orchid Tree. A white-flowering variety is to be seen as well.

It is a much branched small tree growing to about 15 ft. (5 m.) and is found commonly in gardens.

Illustrated on previous page, also on pages 126 & 127

Australian Flame Tree

Brachychiton acerifolium
Family: Sterculiaceae

Of Australian origin, this tree blooms at infrequent intervals, so you have to be fortunate to see it in all its glory. But once seen it is a sight not easily forgotten.

The fully grown tree may be as much as 100 ft. (33 m.) high and so visible over a considerable distance. It is even more conspicuous when flowering as the bare leafless branches are entirely covered with small, fiery red, bell-shaped flowers forming a crimson mass of bloom on the slender structure.

Illustrated on following page, also on half-title page 1

Bottlebrush Tree

Callistemon citrinus
Family: Myrtaceae

This is a purely ornamental tree planted in parks and gardens for its decorative effect. It comes from Australia, where it comprises one of 12 species of the genus *Callistemon*.

It owes its beauty to the numerous red (rarely white) flowers arranged round the stem like a bottlebrush, hence the popular name for this plant. Inflorescences in some varieties are pendent and in others upright. Their axes continue to grow beyond the bloom and these produce leaves. The round, button-like, woody fruits persist on the stem for a long time. The plant can grow to a height of over 20 ft. (7 m.).

Illustrated on previous page

Cape Chestnut

Calodendron capense
Family: Rutaceae

Often found growing wild throughout the mountain forests of the country, this indigenous deciduous tree is also cultivated in parks and gardens for its attractive appearance.

It can reach a height of 60 ft. (20 m.) and the sweet-scented pink blossoms grow conspicuously at ends of branches. Its timber is of limited use.

Illustrated on following page

Cassia

Cassia spectabilis
Family: Caesalpiniaceae

This fast-growing, smallish, deciduous tree originates from tropical America and reaches a height of about 30 ft. (10 m.). Its rounded and somewhat spreading outline bears large, handsome and erect terminal spikes of bright yellow blossoms and is a magnificent sight when in bloom. It is a prominent sight in and around Nairobi.

Illustrated on previous page

Chorisia, Floss-silk Tree

Chorisia speciosa
Family: Bombacaceae

Often confused with Bombax which it resembles, this tree comes from Brazil. It can attain a height of over 45 ft. (15 m.). The branches have a wide span and the swollen, smooth, green trunk is covered with spines. The flowers have five petals and their colour can vary from red to pink. The large fruit provides kapok, fine cotton-like material surrounding the seeds, which is used for stuffing cushions, toys, etc.

Illustrated on following page

Flamboyant, Flame Tree

Delonix regia
Family: Caesalpiniaceae

The original home of this magnificently spectacular tree is Madagascar, where it was first discovered in 1824. It has since been cultivated all over the tropical areas of the world including Kenya.

With its umbrella-shaped span of almost 30 ft. (10 m.), a height of between 30–50 ft. (10–15 m.), and its canopy of scarlet flowers appearing before the leaves develop, the Flamboyant is truly well-named. In Kenya it thrives best at an altitude below 4,500 ft. (1,370 m.), especially where it is warm and dry. Mombasa has a number of these trees planted in the town and they are a striking sight in the right season.

Being deciduous, the tree sheds its leaves during the dry season, when its long brown pods, almost 20 in. (50 cm.) in length, become markedly conspicuous.

Illustrated on previous page

Red Hot Poker Tree, Kaffir Boom

Erythrina abyssinica
Family: Papilionaceae

This attractive, indigenous, deciduous tree is very widespread in Kenya. It is readily recognized, even when not in bloom by its thick and corky bark with deep fissures, and spines. The tree can attain a height of 45 ft. (15 m.).

The bright red flowers stand upright like pokers, hence the name. The inflorescence can be 6 in. (15 cm.) high, in which the flowers are over 2 in. (5 cm.) long. Besides being found in the bush, it is planted for decorative purposes in gardens and parks, where the red blooms readily catch the eye when the tree is bare of leaves.

The bright red and black seeds are uniform in size and so were said to be once used to weigh gold and jewellery. They are often known as 'lucky beans'.

Illustrated on following page

Red Flowering Gum, Flowering Eucalyptus

Eucalyptus ficifolia
Family: Myrtaceae

Unlike other members of this family from Australia, this plant does not grow to great heights, its maximum being around 30 ft. (10 m.). It is planted mainly in gardens and parks for its ornamental look, the terminal group of flowers being a lovely pinkish-red.

Illustrated on previous page

Blue Gum

Eucalyptus spp.
Family: Myrtaceae

A number of Eucalyptus have been introduced into Kenya from their native Australia. They are very common in towns, where they provide shade and decoration. Many different varieties in their diverse shapes and sizes are to be seen in and around Nairobi. One common characteristic of them is the continuous breaking off in strips of the bark from the trunk and branches.

They are fast growing hardwoods, some species attaining a height of over 300 ft. (100 m.), and are used in forestry plantations. Blue Gums produce more firewood at a faster rate than any other tree now planted in Kenya. Although suitable for cutting poles and posts, and for draining the soil, their most important economic value is undoubtedly as wood-fuel. They affect crop yields adversely and therefore must be sited with care when planting.

Illustrated on following page

Jacaranda

Jacaranda mimosifolia
Family: Bignoniaceae

The delicate, bell-shaped, blue-violet flowers of this tree open shortly before the leaves, and a mass of these blossoms against the azure blue of the tropical sky is a memorable sight.

The tree is a native of Brazil and can reach a height of up to 30 ft. (10 m.). It flowers after the 'short rains' in Kenya, about October to November and the drab streets in and around towns then acquire a most attractive quality. Nairobi parks and gardens have many Jacaranda, and the main avenue leading into the industrial town of Nakuru is transformed in the flowering season.

Prunus, Himalayan Bird Cherry

Prunus puddum
Family: Rosaceae

This quick-growing, well-shaped, deciduous tree reaches a height of about 30 ft. (10 m.). Twice a year, at the beginning of the rains, its bare branches are covered with abundant pink blossoms which give the tree an appearance of delicate beauty. It is frequently seen in gardens and lining road verges in residential areas.

Illustrated on following page and pages 5

Pepper Tree

Schinus molle
Family: Anacardiaceae

A very ornamental tree, which needs plenty of room to grow to its proper shape and because it is a very bad neighbour to other plants. Reaching a height of over 30 ft. (10 m.), it resembles the weeping willow because of its drooping branches. The prominent and attractive, round berries, which are red when mature, hang in loose clusters.

It smells strongly of resin, for the production of which it is used in its native Peru. It is quite common in gardens and parks.

Illustrated on previous page and page 125

Nandi Flame Tree, African Tulip Tree

Spathodea campanulata
Family: Bignoniaceae

This indigenous deciduous tree is a spectacular sight with its large, orange-red flowers with gold margins, set off against dark green heavy foliage, appearing after the start of the rainy season. It is not only common in forests, but also in parks and residential areas, where it is planted in large numbers. It can grow to a height of 50 ft. (15 m.) and the cluster of flowers, borne at the end of branches towards the top of the tree, may be 6–8 in. (15–20 cm.) across.

The unopened flower-buds contain water under pressure and this spurts out if a bud is punctured, giving the plant the name of 'Fountain Tree' in some places. Originally a native of West Africa, where it was discovered in the jungle and first described by Palisot Beavois in 1757. The tree was regarded as an agent of supernatural powers in the Gold Coast, the flowers being used by witch doctors for black magic, and the wood for making tribal drums.

Illustrated on following page and on back cover

Pride of Bolivia, Tipu Tree

Tipuana tipu
Family: Papilionaceae

A beautiful tree, with a splendid crown of light small-leaved foliage, which bears plentiful clusters of yellow, pea-shaped flowers. It is of medium size, reaching a height of 30–40 ft. (10–13 m.). As its common name suggests it comes from Bolivia. It is an attractive sight along roads and in parks when in full blossom.

Illustrated on previous page

3 SHRUBS

Acalypha

Acalypha spp.
Family: Euphorbiaceae

There are over 200 species of *Acalypha*, all in the tropics. These are shrubs with markedly variegated foliage, ranging from deep-pink, red, brown, greenish-brown, to various shades of green. The species *A. wilkesiana* is known as Copperleaf and originates in the South Sea Islands.

The shrubs can grow to a height of over 6 ft. (2 m.) and are often trimmed into hedges. Very popular in gardens where they provide a most attractive sight.

Illustrated on following page

Desert Rose, Mock Azalea

Adenium obesum
Family: Apocynaceae

A shrub, which grows in the dry parts of East Africa, has a succulent, swollen stem and bears attractive pink flowers. The milky juice or sap is highly toxic and is used as an arrow poison.

Illustrated on previous page

Yesterday, Today and Tomorrow

Brunfelsia hopeana
Solanaceae

This evergreen shrub from Brazil bears dark purple-blue flowers, changing to mauve, cream and white as they age, which accounts for the plant's popular name. At night the blossoms produce a heady fragrance.

Illustrated on following page

Candle Bush

Cassia didymobotrya
Family: Caesalpiniaceae

This is an indigenous shrub growing wild to a height of 6–9 ft. (2–3 m.). It is common in grassland, scrub, at the edge of forests, and often obvious along country roads during the flowering season.

The bright yellow flowers form dense clusters of upright spikes giving the effect of a candelabrum with numerous candles.

Illustrated on previous page

Moonflower, Angel's Trumpet

Datura suaveolens
Family: Solanaceae

A soft-wood, fast-growing shrub from 4–12 ft. (1.3–4 m.) in height, it bears large, pendent, trumpet-shaped flowers. The white variety is very sweetly scented in the evening.

This is a common, but very poisonous garden plant. It is available in a variety of different colours, including white, yellow and pink, and in single and double forms.

Illustrated on following page

Red Euphorbia

Euphorbia cotonifolia
Family: Euphorbiaceae

Of West Indian origin, this deciduous shrub can grow to a height of
10 ft. (3 m.). It is most attractive with its maroon-red leaves, which
gradually turn brown and eventually fall off. An ornamental plant,
it is widely used in gardens.

Illustrated on previous page

Snow on the Mountain

Euphorbia leucocephala
Family: Euphorbiaceae

This easily grown deciduous plant from Guatemala is reminiscent of a miniature Poinsettia, with tiny cream bracts, sometimes tinted rose, completely covering the 3–8 ft. (1–3 m.) high, compact bushes, and making an arresting sight.

Illustrated on following page

Poinsettia, Christmas Star

Euphorbia pulcherrima
Euphorbiaceae

The Poinsettia is as characteristic of Christmas in the tropics as the holly is in northern latitudes, although it blooms in Kenya during July. It is widely used as decorations on tables, in rooms and on Christmas cards and calendars. The bright red bracts forming a rosette suggest a star.

The shrub, a native of tropical America, has coloured bracts ranging from scarlet to pink to pale yellow and can acquire a height of 9–12 ft. (3–4 m.) if not pruned. The flowers are insignificant, the bracts making the plant so conspicuous.

Illustrated on previous page

Hibiscus, Chinese Rose

Hibiscus rosa-sinensis
Family: Malvaceae

Hibiscus is probably the world's best-known tropical flower. Also known as the 'Rose of China', from where it originates, it has spread and is cultivated throughout the tropics. This shrub produces a host of beautiful flowers of various colours, but all with prominent yellow stamens and red stigmas. It is these blooms that Hawaiian maidens weave into garlands with which they traditionally greet visitors to their island.

Continued on page 72

Continued from page 69

Hibiscus, Chinese Rose

The plant is sometimes used for hedging and can grow to a height of 12–15 ft. (4–5 m.). The flowers are not suitable for cutting, as they stay at their best for only a day or so, either on the bush or in a vase.

This Chinese Hibiscus occurs in numerous forms, including double ones, in a large variety of colours and is very suitable for gardens and parks. The family also has a number of species indigenous to Kenya.

Illustrated on previous two pages

Christ Thorn, Crown of Thorns

Euphorbia splendens
Family: Euphorbiaceae

Perhaps the best-known member of the genus *Euphorbia*, this shrub with its formidably sharp thorns, and growing to a height of 6 ft. (2 m.), makes an excellent hedge. It can also be clipped back to edge flower-beds or allowed to grow into a large, attractive bush covered in red flowers. It is a native of Madagascar.

Illustrated on following page

Lantana

Lantana spp.
Family: Verbenaceae

Many species of Lantana grow into showy shrubs about 6 ft. (2 m.) high and are very suitable for gardens, but *L. camara* with its prickly square stems, is scheduled as a dangerous weed. Its small pinkish-purple flowers are quite pretty, but the fruit in the form of black berries is widely dispersed by birds, and the shrub colonizes large tracts in the wild. This harmful plant, which originates in South America, has become established in many parts of the world and forms impenetrable thickets in Ceylon and Java.

The cultivated varieties do not proliferate in the same manner and can make colourful additions to gardens with their orange, pale and dark yellow, or white flowers; but pruning is necessary for control.

Illustrated on previous page

Plumbago

Plumbago capensis
Family: Plumbaginaceae

Delicate pale-blue flowers catch your eye as you drive past garden boundaries. This very popular species originates from the Cape Province of South Africa and is extensively used for hedges, and widely cultivated as a decorative plant.

It has relatively weak branches which scramble rather than climb, and the attractive blossoms, which flower almost during the whole year, are arranged in small groups at the end of the stems.

Illustrated on following page

Frangipani, Temple Tree

Plumeria spp.
Family: Apocynaceae

This is a familiar shrub, almost a small tree, having a characteristic appearance with rather thick, smooth, green twigs which branch regularly and ooze large quantities of latex if damaged. It is often planted near temples and in cemeteries in India and South East Asia.

The white variety (*P. alba*) originates from the West Indies and is named after the Frenchman Plumier, who was a pioneer of West Indian botany. The pink-flowered Frangipani (*P. rubra*) comes from Central America and now has a wide range of allied colours.

It is suggested that the name Frangipani originates from the French *frangipanier*, meaning coagulated milk; but a more attractive hypothesis refers to a perfume developed from its flowers in the 12th century by an Italian nobleman named Frangipani.

Illustrated on previous page

Bird of Paradise, Crane Flower

Strelitzia reginae
Family : Musaceae

This plant is a native of South Africa. The highly decorative inflorescence appears on a long stalk among leaves somewhat similar to those of the Banana.

The flower's resemblance to a bird's head is uncanny and once seen and identified, it cannot be forgotten. Words are inadequate to describe such an exotic bloom and the reader is referred to the illustration on the next page.

It is interesting to discover how the scientific name of the Bird of Paradise flower came about. Rev. John Lightfoot, an Englishman, who produced the first flora of Scotland in 1778, sold his herbarium to George III, who in turn presented it to his Queen, Caroline of Mecklehburg-Strelitz in the late 18th century. She was the first royal owner of what is now Buckingham Palace, and the Bird of Paradise is called *Strelitzia reginae* after her.

Illustrated on following page

Fire Bush, Oranges and Lemons

Streptosolon jamesonii
Family: Solanaceae

A much branched evergreen shrub, up to 6 ft. (2 m.) tall, it originates from Columbia. It bears bright clusters of orange-yellow flowers in great profusion. An attractive yellow-flowered variety is also to be seen. A popular plant, common in most gardens.

Illustrated on previous page

Yellow Bells, Yellow Elder

Tecoma stans
Family: Bignoniaceae

Introduced into Kenya from tropical America, this attractive ornamental shrub can grow to a height of several feet. It is found in many gardens because of its decorative yellow, bell-shaped, Gloxinia-like flowers, arranged in terminal inflorescences.

Illustrated on following page

Cape Honeysuckle

Tecomaria capensis
Family: Bignoniaceae

As its name suggests, this shrub originates from South Africa. In full sun and dry conditions, it produces a wonderful show of five-lobed, orange-red spikes of flowers in terminal clusters. Because of its climbing habit, it makes an excellent hedge.

Illustrated on previous page

Thevetia, Yellow Oleander

Thevetia peruviana
Family: Apocynaceae

With its origin in tropical America, this shrub grows about 12 ft. (4 m.) high. Its elongated leaves, shiny on the upper side, are reminiscent of the Oleander. The five-lobed lemon-yellow blossoms, which flower for most of the year, have a sweet scent. The plant contains a glycocide in its milky sap and all parts of it are dangerously poisonous.

A very decorative shrub, it appears in many gardens and parks, and Nairobi makes a feature of them along its roadsides.

Illustrated on following page

4 CLIMBERS

Gloriosa Lily, Flame Lily

Gloriosa virescens
Family: Liliaceae

A very attractive lily-like climbing plant which is native in tropical Africa and Asia. The showy red and yellow flowers are solitary. With the advent of the rains the blooms begin to appear, the small plant climbing with long tendrils growing from the tips of its leaves. In Europe, it is cultivated in greenhouses and offered in flower-shops as a cut-flower.

Illustrated on previous page

Bougainvillea

Bougainvillea spp.
Family: Nyctaginaceae

A thorny shrub which can climb by means of its long, sharp spines to the top of the tallest tree. Usually, however, it is seen as a hedge or a garden shrub, sending up in the air or over a wall curved branches laden with flowers.

The commonly cultivated Bougainvillea are derived from hybrids of *B. glabra* and *B. spectabilis*; and there are scores of different forms and colours. The riot of colour for which they are well known, ranging from a deep magenta-purple, through crimson and soft-pink to brick-red and bronzy-gold, even white, is not provided by the flowers as is generally thought, but by three, large, colourful bracts. The true flowers are quite inconspicuous.

Continued on page 96

Illustrated on following two pages   **93**

Continued from page 93

Bougainvillea

Bougainvillea is a native of Brazil and was first brought to the notice of the world by the 18th century French navigator Louis de Bouganville, who found specimens in Rio de Janeiro. Now it is cultivated all over the tropic and sub-tropic world.

Bougainvillea are very common in gardens and parks, and they make a spectacular show along roads in Kenya towns, especially Nairobi. The plant loves warmth and thrives best during the warm dry months.

Illustrated on previous two pages

Petrea, Purple Wreath

Petrea volubilis
Family : Verbenaceae

One of the most beautiful of all climbers, with large tresses of deep-violet flowers. The leaves are rough and papery, and because of its woody nature the plant can also be grown as a shrub. It originates from South America.

Illustrated on following page and page 128

Golden Shower

Pyrostegia venusta
Family: Bignoniaceae

Perhaps the best-known of the Bignonia family, this native of Brazil grows freely and blooms in profusion in full sun. The gorgeous orange-coloured, tubular flowers in large clusters catch the eye everywhere, on roofs, hedges, pergolas and even trees. It is drought-resistant and so in flower for most of the year.

Illustrated on previous page

5 SUCCULENTS & CACTI

Sisal

Agave sisalana
Family: Agavaceae

A native of Mexico, this plant is generally grown in hot climates in large plantations for fibre production. Various members of the Agave family are also planted in large gardens and parks because of their decorative value.

Its very elongated, dark-green leaves measure up to 5 ft. (1.5 m.) and bear sharp spikes at their tips. The inflorescence of this succulent is very tall, almost 20 ft. (6 m.) in height, and bears yellowish flowers. The name Sisal arises from the name of the port in Mexico from which it was originally exported.

The coarse, yellow-white fibres, 3–6 ft. (1–2 m.) long, are obtained from the leaves through a process of crushing, and made pliable by beating and brushing. When dry they are used in the manufacture of twine, rope, and also nets, hammocks and carpets. The demand for Sisal has dropped considerably in recent years due to the availability of synthetic fibres.

Illustrated on following page

Aloe

Aloe spp.
Family Liliaceae

Aloes are African members of the Lily family, and are often grown in gardens as ornamental plants. There are many Aloe species in Kenya and they flower after the rain. The inflorescence appears on a tall stem and is generally orange-red, and infrequently yellow.

The spiny, sharp-pointed, succulent leaves contain a juice which has long been regarded as having curative properties, and is used to relieve burns, insect bites and other inflammatory conditions. It is now grown commercially for use in beauty preparations such as suntan lotions.

Illustrated on previous page

Giant Cactus

Cereus peruvianus
Family: Cactaceae

This is a sturdy, tall-growing, branched species which may reach a height of 12–20 ft. (4–7 m.). It originates from South America. The 5–7 sided branches are covered in spines and develop large, whitish, trumpet-shaped flowers on their edges, which only blossom at night.

Illustrated on following page

Candelabra Tree, Tree Euphorbia

Euphorbia candelabrum
Family: Euphorbiaceae

A cactus-like succulent tree, growing as high as 45 ft. (15 m.) in savannah country, sometimes on a termite mound, this plant is very common in certain areas of the Rift Valley. Lake Nakuru National Park has a Euphorbia forest which must be one of the largest in Africa.

The tree has a relatively short, thick trunk from which spread a number of spiny branches in a candelabra fashion.

Illustrated on previous page

Prickly Pear

Opuntia ficus-indica
Family: Cactaceae

A plant which can grow to a height of 15 ft. (5 m.), it is a member of the Cactus family. What appear to be leaves are really stems and branches, with the leaves transformed into spines and bristles. The yellow to orange flowers turn into pear-shaped fruits, which are edible after careful removal of the spines.

It originates from America and is now regarded in Kenya, especially in the Rift Valley, as a noxious weed because it propogates so readily. The plant makes a good protective hedge.

Illustrated on following page

Adam's Needle, Spanish Bayonet

Yucca aloifolia
Family: Liliaceae

Its natural distribution extending from Mexico to Guatemala, this plant, often cultivated as a hedge, can reach a height of 12 ft. (4 m.). It bears a close resemblance to an Agave.

The mature plant produces a compact inflorescence 24–36 in. (60–90 cm) high, composed of numerous creamy-white, pendulous flowers, which attract attention in Kenyan gardens and parks.

Illustrated on previous page

6 MISCELLANEOUS

Agapanthus, African Lily

Agapanthus africanus
Family: Amaryllidaceae

This member of the Lily family is a native of southern Africa. The 8 in. (20 cm.) head, on a longish stalk, is made up of many tubular flowers, which may be blue or white.

This is a very ornamental plant, growing readily in most areas and is a great favourite in private gardens and parks.

Illustrated on following page

Feathery Bamboo

Bambusa vulgaris
Family: Gramineae

A vigorous growing bamboo, used for making fences, scaffoldings, and for other building purposes, it reaches a height of 50 ft. (15 m.) or more where rainfall is adequate. It has green stems. A handsome variety known as 'Golden Bamboo' has yellow stems. It originates from South Asia.

Illustrated on previous page

Canna

Canna spp.
Family: Cannaceae

A highly decorative plant found in most gardens, it comes from tropical America. Many types and varieties grow readily in Kenya and provide an infinite variety of strikingly coloured flowers, and foliage which may be tall, dwarf, green or bronze. The wild Canna (*C. bidentata*) is a widespread plant in fields.

Illustrated on following page

Epidendrum

Epidendrum spp.
Family: Orchidaceae

This is an easily grown orchid from South America, with erect, relatively thin, single or few branched stems and numerous white aerial roots at the base. It attains a height of about 4 ft. (1.3 m.). Many varieties bearing different coloured flowers have been cultivated.

Illustrated on previous page

Water Lily

Nymphaea spp.
Family : Nymphaeaceae

The name *Nymphaea* is derived from 'nymphaia', for according to Greek legend, the flower arose from a nymph, who had died of jealousy. Another legend suggests that she died from unrequited love for Hercules.

The water lily family is well distributed throughout almost the whole world including the tropics, in freshwater lakes and ponds. The long stalks arising from the rootstock end in circular, oval or heart-shaped blades which float on the surface of the water. The strikingly lovely flowers, blue, yellow, or pink, rise above it.

Illustrated on following page

Index

Opposite: Pepper Tree with its red fruit
Pages 126 & 127: Camel's Foot blossoms
Page 128: The deep-violet flowers of Petrea